Theory Paper   Grade 8   2015   A

Duration 3 hours

TOTAL MARKS
100

Candidates should answer all FIVE questions.
Write your answers on this paper – no others will be accepted.
Answers must be written clearly and neatly – otherwise marks may be lost.

1   Complete the violin parts in the following extract adapted from a trio sonata by Corelli, following the figuring shown under the basso continuo.

15

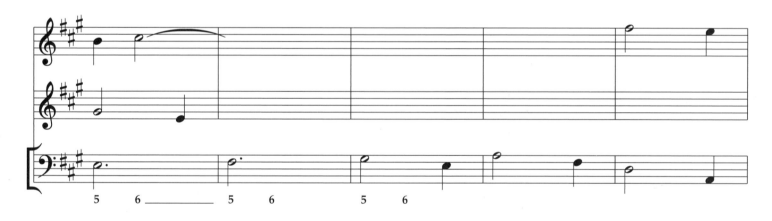

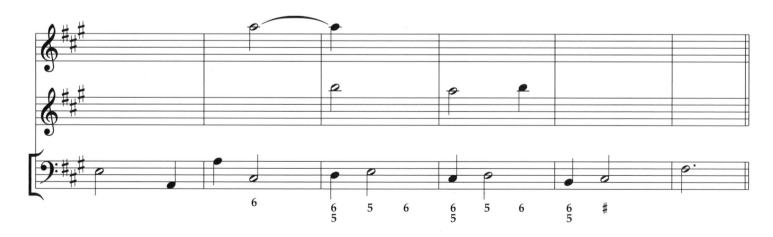

2 Complete the given outline of the following passage, adapted from a piano piece by Clementi (1752–1832).

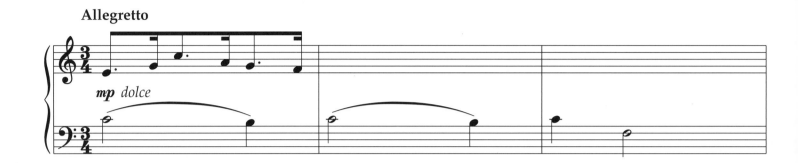

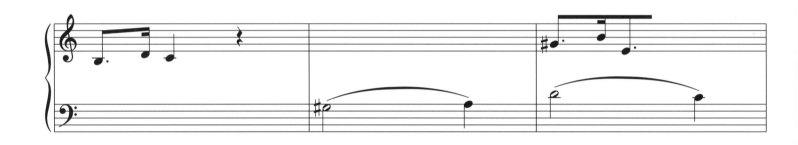

Music Theory Past Papers 2015

ABRSM Grade 8

3 Compose a complete melody of not less than 12 bars using **ONE** of the following openings and for the given unaccompanied instrument. Continue in the same style and include appropriate performance directions. Write the complete melody on the staves below.

CLARINET (at concert pitch)

TRUMPET (at concert pitch)

Andante cantabile

etc.

4 Look at the extract printed opposite, which is from a string quartet, and then answer the questions below.

(a) Identify the chords marked ∗ in bars 5 and 11 (shaded) by writing on the dotted lines below. Use either words or symbols. For each chord, indicate the position, show whether it is major, minor, augmented or diminished, and name the prevailing key in bar 11.

Bar 5 .... (3)

Bar 11 .... Key .... (4)

(b) Write out in full the first violin part of bar 8 as you think it should be played.

(3)

(c) Mark **clearly** on the score, using the appropriate capital letter for identification, one example of each of the following. Also give the bar number(s) of each of your answers. The first answer is given.

From bar 5 onwards

A a group of notes in the second violin part which are marked to be played slightly separated (circle the notes concerned).   Bar ....9....

B a place where the cello and viola sound a note in unison (circle the notes concerned).   Bar .... (2)

C four consecutive notes in the first violin part that form the chord of a dominant 7th (V7) in the tonic key (circle the notes concerned).   Bar .... (2)

D a rising chromatic semitone (augmented unison) in the second violin part (circle the notes concerned).   Bar .... (2)

E melodic imitation between the first violin and cello parts, across three bars (mark ⌐ E ⌐ over the bars).   Bars .... (2)

F a place where the viola has to use an open string (circle the note concerned).   Bar .... (2)

(d) Answer TRUE or FALSE to each of the following statements:

(i) The cello part is the only one that does *not* use syncopation in this extract. .... (2)

(ii) The second violin and viola parts do not cross in this extract. .... (2)

(e) From the list below, underline the name of the most likely composer of this piece.

Brahms   Elgar   Debussy   Mozart (1)

5 Look at the extract printed on pages 9–10, which is from Walton's *Variations on a Theme by Hindemith*, and then answer the questions below. $\boxed{25}$

(a) Give the meaning of:

tr~~~~~ (bar 1, timpani)   .... (2)

♪ (e.g. bar 4, second violins)   .... (2)

Muta in Cfg. (contrafagotto) (bar 8, third bassoon)   ....

.... (2)

(b) Write out the parts for first and second clarinets and first and second horns in bars 1–2 as they would sound at concert pitch.

Clarinets 1 2   (3)

Horns 1 2   (2)

(c) Complete the following statements:

   (i)   On the first beat of bar 2, the lowest-sounding note is played by the ....,

         the .... and the .... (3)

   (ii) On the third beat of bar 7, the highest-sounding note is played by the .... (2)

   (iii) Two woodwind instruments play a mordent simultaneously in bar .... (2)

   (iv) A standard orchestral brass instrument *not* playing in this extract is the .... (1)

(d) Describe fully the numbered and bracketed harmonic intervals *sounding* between:

   1   double basses and second bassoon, bar 5   .... (2)

   2   second violins and third bassoon, bar 6   .... (2)

   3   violas and cor anglais, bar 7   .... (2)

Theory Paper   Grade 8   2015   B

Duration 3 hours

Candidates should answer all FIVE questions.
Write your answers on this paper – no others will be accepted.
Answers must be written clearly and neatly – otherwise marks may be lost.

TOTAL MARKS
100

1   Complete the violin parts in the following extract adapted from a trio sonata by Purcell, following the figuring shown under the basso continuo.

15

etc.

2 Complete the given outline of the following passage, adapted from a piano piece by Beethoven (1770–1827). Note that some of the left-hand part is in the treble clef.

etc.

3 Compose a complete melody of not less than 12 bars using **ONE** of the following openings  and for the given unaccompanied instrument. Continue in the same style and include appropriate performance directions. Write the complete melody on the staves below.

CELLO

OBOE

Andante (quasi Allegretto) consolante

4 Look at the extract printed opposite, which is from Weber's Piano Sonata, Op. 70, and then answer the questions below.

(a) Name two similarities and three differences between bars 1–4 and 16–20 (both marked ⌐   ⌐).

Similarities   1   ....   (1)

　　　　　　2   ....   (1)

Differences   1   ....   (1)

　　　　　　2   ....   (1)

　　　　　　3   ....   (1)

(b) Write out in full the top line of the right-hand part of bar 14 as you think it should be played.

(3)

(c) Identify the chords marked ∗ in bars 7 (shaded) and 21 by writing on the dotted lines below. Use either words or symbols. For each chord, indicate the position, show whether it is major, minor, augmented or diminished, and name the prevailing key in bar 7.

Bar 7   ....   Key   ....   (4)

Bar 21   ....   (3)

(d) Mark **clearly** on the score, using the appropriate capital letter for identification, one example of each of the following. Also give the bar number(s) of each of your answers. The first answer is given.

From bar 9 onwards

A　a harmonic interval of a diminished 5th in
　　　the left-hand part (circle the notes concerned).　Bar ....17....

B　a perfect cadence in the dominant key.　Bars ....   (2)

C　a written-out upper mordent.　Bar ....   (2)

D　a chromatic lower auxiliary note in the
　　　right-hand part (circle the note concerned).　Bar ....   (2)

E　simultaneous unaccented passing notes between the hands that
　　　form the harmonic interval of a major sixth (circle the notes concerned).　Bar ....   (2)

F　a place where the music passes through the relative minor
　　　key (mark ⌐   F   ⌐ over the bar(s) concerned).　Bar(s) ....   (2)

15

5 Look at the extract printed on pages 17–18, which is from Stravinsky's *Le baiser de la fée*, and then answer the questions below.

(a) Give the meaning of:

a 2 (e.g. bar 1, oboes) .... (2)

molto (e.g. bar 6, violas) .... (1)

(b) Complete the following statements:

(i)   The viola and second violin parts cross in bar .... (2)

(ii) There is syncopation in a brass part in bar(s) .... (2)

(c) (i)   Write out the parts for first, second and third horns in bars 3–4 as they would sound at concert pitch.

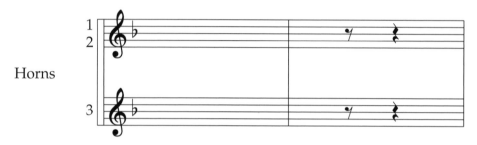

(3)

(ii) Using the blank staves at the foot of page 18, write out the parts for clarinets in bar 6 as they would sound at concert pitch and using the given clefs. (5)

(d) Answer TRUE or FALSE to each of the following statements:

(i)   The first flute and first violins sound in unison in bars 1–2. .... (2)

(ii) The notes played by the brass section on the
first beat of bar 4 form a chord of D minor in first inversion. .... (2)

(e) Describe fully the numbered and bracketed harmonic intervals *sounding* between:

1 first clarinet and cor anglais, bar 2 .... (2)

2 first oboe and second flute, bar 4 .... (2)

3 violas and trombone, bar 4 .... (2)

17

etc.

(c) (ii)
Bar 6

Clarinets

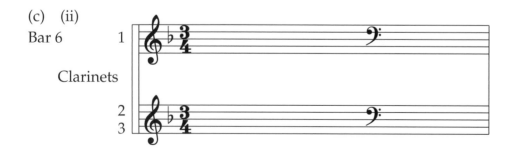

Theory Paper   Grade 8   2015   C

TOTAL MARKS
100

Duration 3 hours

Candidates should answer all FIVE questions.
Write your answers on this paper – no others will be accepted.
Answers must be written clearly and neatly – otherwise marks may be lost.

1   Complete the violin parts in the following extract adapted from a trio sonata by Caldara,   15
    following the figuring shown under the basso continuo.

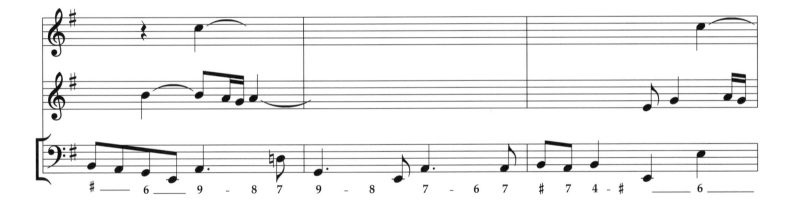

2 Complete the given outline of the following passage, adapted from a piano piece by Kirnberger (1721–1783).

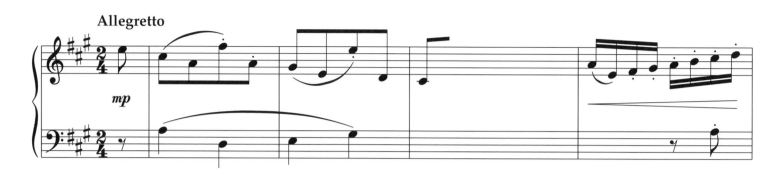

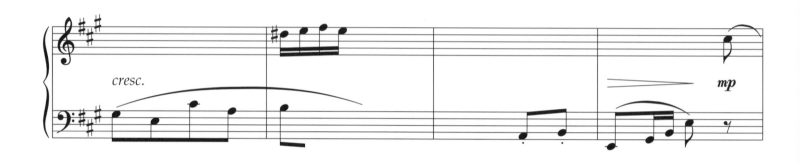

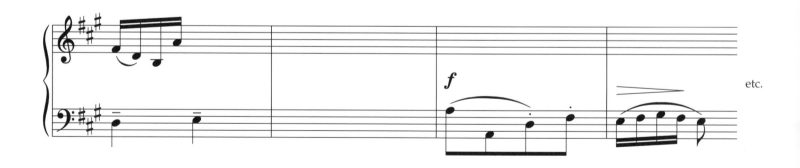

3 Compose a complete melody of not less than 12 bars using **ONE** of the following openings and for the given unaccompanied instrument. Continue in the same style and include appropriate performance directions. Write the complete melody on the staves below.

FLUTE

Molto vivace

Bruckner (adapted)

TROMBONE

Andante

4 Look at the extract printed opposite, which is from a piano sonata, and then answer the questions below.

(a) Identify the chords marked * in bars 9 and 19 by writing on the dotted lines below. Use either words or symbols. For each chord, indicate the position, show whether it is major, minor, augmented or diminished, and name the prevailing key.

Bar 9 .... Key .... (4)

Bar 19 .... Key .... (4)

(b) Mark **clearly** on the score, using the appropriate capital letter for identification, one example of each of the following. Also give the bar number(s) of each of your answers. The first answer is given.

From bar 13 onwards

A a melodic interval of a compound diminished 5th
 in the left-hand part (circle the notes concerned). Bar ...22....

B a bar where all the notes form a diminished 7th chord. Bar .... (2)

C a false (cross) relation between the top note of the right-hand part
 and the bottom note of the left-hand part (circle the notes concerned). Bar .... (2)

D a rising chromatic semitone (augmented unison) in the
 top line of the right-hand part (circle the notes concerned). Bar(s) .... (2)

(c) Name two similarities and three differences between bars 9–10 and 11–12.

Similarities 1 .... (1)

 2 .... (1)

Differences 1 .... (1)

 2 .... (1)

 3 .... (1)

(d) Complete the following statements regarding the *right-hand motif in bars 2–3* (marked ⌐ ⌐):

 (i) The motif is later repeated two octaves lower in the left-hand part in bars .... (2)

 (ii) The motif also occurs as part of a rising melodic sequence (not exact) in bars .... (2)

(e) From the list below, underline the name of the most likely composer of this piece and give a reason for your choice.

 Ravel   Brahms   Chopin   Wagner (1)

 Reason:

 .... (1)

5 Look at the extract printed on pages 25–6, which is from C. H. H. Parry's *Overture to an Unwritten Tragedy*, and then answer the questions below.

(a) Give the meaning of:

tr〰〰〰 (bar 1, timpani) .... (2)

♪ (e.g. bar 5, second violins) .... (2)

(b) (i) Write out the parts for first and second clarinets and bass clarinet from the beginning of the extract to the first note of bar 2 as they would sound at concert pitch and using the given clefs.

(3)

(ii) Write out the parts for first and second horns in bar 3 as they would sound at concert pitch.

(2)

(c) Complete the following statements:

(i) On the first beat of bar 3, the lowest-sounding note is played by the ....,

the ...., the .... and the

.... (4)

(ii) The notes played on the first quaver of bar 6 form a .... chord in the key of C major. (2)

(iii) There is a harmonic interval of a compound augmented 5th between two of the same double-reed instruments in bar .... (2)

(iv) The instruments *sounding* in unison with the violas on the first note of bar 4 are

the ...., the ....,

the .... and the .... (4)

(d) Describe fully the numbered and bracketed harmonic intervals *sounding* between:

1 first trombone and first clarinet, bar 4 .... (2)

2 fourth horn and first bassoon, bar 5 .... (2)

24

Theory Paper   Grade 8   2015   S

Duration 3 hours

TOTAL MARKS
100

Candidates should answer all FIVE questions.
Write your answers on this paper – no others will be accepted.
Answers must be written clearly and neatly – otherwise marks may be lost.

1 Complete the violin parts in the following extract adapted from a trio sonata by Corelli, following the figuring shown under the basso continuo.

15

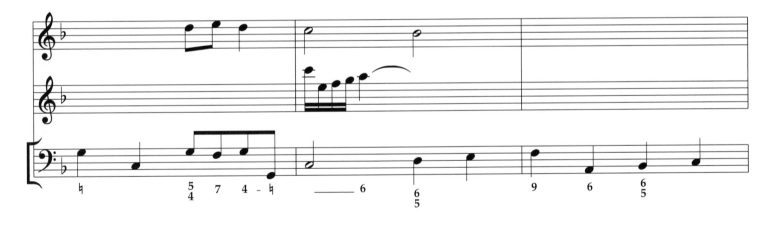

2 Complete the given outline of the following passage, adapted from a piano piece by Czerny (1791–1857).

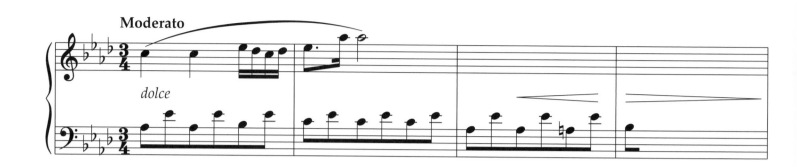

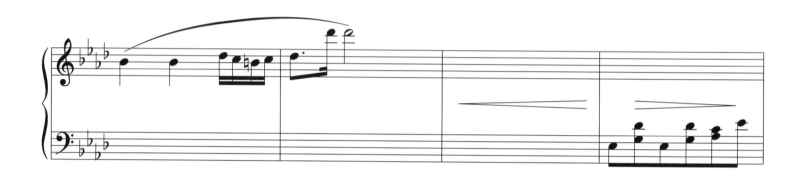

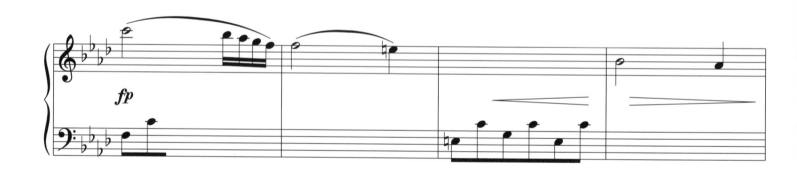

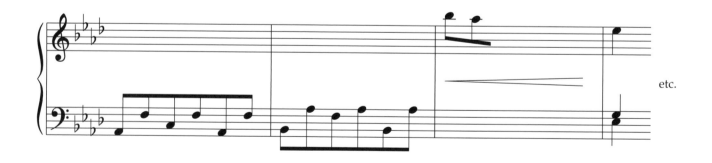

3 Compose a complete melody of not less than 12 bars using **ONE** of the following openings and for the given unaccompanied instrument. Continue in the same style and include appropriate performance directions. Write the complete melody on the staves below.

TRUMPET (at concert pitch)

VIOLIN

Vivace
In tempo, ma cantabile

30

4 Look at the extract printed opposite, which is from Hummel's *Rondo Brillante*, Op. 109, and then answer the questions below.

(a) Identify the chords marked * in bars 13 and 21 (shaded) by writing on the dotted lines below. Use either words or symbols. For each chord, indicate the position, show whether it is major, minor, augmented or diminished, and name the prevailing key in bar 21.

Bar 13 .... (3)

Bar 21 .... Key .... (4)

(b) Name one similarity and three differences between bars 1–4 and bars 17–20.

Similarity .... (1)

Differences 1 .... (1)

         2 .... (1)

         3 .... (1)

(c) Mark **clearly** on the score, using the appropriate capital letter for identification, one example of each of the following. Also give the bar number of each of your answers. The first answer is given.

From bar 9 onwards

  A a melodic interval of a perfect 4th in the
      left-hand inner part (circle the notes concerned). Bar ...22...

  B an upward-resolving appoggiatura in the right-hand part
      that forms the harmonic interval of a compound major 7th
      with the bottom note of the left-hand part (circle the note concerned). Bar .... (2)

  C a descending chromatic semitone (augmented unison)
      in the right-hand inner part (circle the notes concerned). Bar .... (2)

  D four successive quavers in the left-hand part that form a
      dominant 7th chord (V7) in the tonic key (circle the notes concerned). Bar .... (2)

(d) Write out in full the top line of the right-hand part of bar 10 as you think it should be played.

(3)

(e) Complete the following statements:

  (i)   The music begins in the key of D major and there
       is an imperfect cadence (Ic–V) in the tonic key in bar .... (1)

  (ii) In bars 11–12 it passes through the key of ....

       and in bars 13–14 through the key of .... (2)

  (iii) In bars 15–16 there is a(n) .... cadence in the key of .... (2)

5 Look at the extract printed opposite, which is from a ballet, and then answer the questions below. [25]

(a) Give the meaning of:

Tambour de Basque .... (2)

col legno (e.g. bar 3, first violins) .... (2)

sourdine (bar 5, horns) .... (2)

o (bar 5, second harp) .... (2)

(b) (i) Write out the part for first clarinet in bars 1–2 as it would sound at concert pitch.

(2)

(ii) Write out the parts for horns in bars 5–6 as they would sound at concert pitch.

(3)

(c) Mark **clearly** on the score, using the appropriate capital letter for identification, one example of each of the following. Also give the bar number of each of your answers. The first answer is given.

A   a bar in which the player is instructed to play the notes slightly separated.   Bar ....3....

B   a melodic interval of an augmented 2nd in a string part (circle the notes concerned).   Bar .... (2)

C   a place where the first bassoon and upper line of the cellos sound a note in unison (circle the notes concerned).   Bar .... (2)

D   an acciaccatura (grace note) that sounds a minor 2nd lower than the main note that follows it (circle the note concerned).   Bar .... (2)

(d) Describe fully the numbered and bracketed harmonic intervals *sounding* between:

1   violas and first bassoon, bar 3   .... (2)

2   second violins and cor anglais, bar 7   .... (2)

(e) From the list below, underline the name of the most likely composer of this piece and give a reason for your choice.

Brahms   Bizet   Debussy   Elgar   (1)

Reason:

.... (1)

33